Journey to the West

LEVEL ONE   400 HEADWORDS

T0345868

Great Clarendon Street, Oxford, OX2 6DP, United Kingdom

Oxford University Press is a department of the University of Oxford.
It furthers the University's objective of excellence in research, scholarship,
and education by publishing worldwide. Oxford is a registered trade
mark of Oxford University Press in the UK and in certain other countries

© Oxford University Press 2014

The moral rights of the author have been asserted

First published in 2014

2022

10 9 8 7 6

ISBN: 978 0 19 424979 9   Book
ISBN: 978 0 19 463942 2   Book and Audio Pack

Printed in China

This book is printed on paper from certified and well-managed sources

ACKNOWLEDGEMENTS

Cover and interior artwork by: Yishan Li/Advocate Art

DOMINOES

Series Editors: Bill Bowler and Sue Parminter

Journey to the West

Retold by Janet Hardy-Gould

Illustrated by Yishan Li

Janet Hardy-Gould has worked as a teacher of English for many years. In her free time she enjoys reading history books and modern novels, visiting other European countries, and drinking tea with her friends. She lives in the ancient town of Lewes in the south of England with her husband and their two children. She has written a number of books, including *Henry VIII and his Six Wives*, and *King Arthur* in the Oxford Bookworms series, and *Ali Baba and the Forty Thieves*, *Crying Wolf and Other Tales*, *The Great Fire of London*, *Sinbad*, *Mulan*, *Hercules*, *Merlin*, and an adaptation of *Sherlock Holmes: The Emerald Crown* in the Dominoes series.

OXFORD
UNIVERSITY PRESS

BEFORE READING

1 Here are the main characters in *Journey to the West*. Match a sentence with each picture. Use a dictionary to help you.

a Triptaka is learning to be a monk, and he doesn't like fighting. ☐

b Sandy lives in a river, and he fights with a spade. ☐

c Monkey can fly through the sky, and he fights with a staff. ☐

d Pigsy lives on a farm, likes eating, and fights with a rake. ☐

2 These characters go on a journey in the story. Where, do you think?

a ☐ From China to England.

b ☐ From China to America.

c ☐ From China to India.

3 What do they do on their journey? Write 'yes' or 'no'. Use a dictionary to help you.

a They stay in some nice hotels. . . . .

b They fight angry demons. . . . .

c They find a lot of treasure. . . . .

d They eat good food every day. . . . .

e They bring back holy writings to China. . . . .

CHAPTER ONE
Monkey and the young monk

Our story begins long ago on the **Mountain** of **Fruit** and Flowers in China. On this mountain there was an old **rock**. It was red from many years in the hot sun. One morning, the rock broke open, and a **monkey** was born from it. The monkey quickly learned to run fast, and to **fight** well. Soon all the monkeys on the mountain came to him. 'You're very **strong**!' they cried.

'That's true,' answered Monkey.

'You're the strongest of us. So you must be our **king**,' the monkeys said.

'All right,' said Monkey.

After some years, Monkey heard stories about a **holy** man far away. 'That man teaches many interesting things,' thought Monkey. 'I must learn from him, and be the strongest king of all!' So Monkey left the mountain, and went to the holy man's home. Monkey was a good student. First, he learned to move quickly through the sky on a white **cloud**. Then he learned to take out some of his hairs, say **magic words** over them, and make hundreds of little monkeys. Last of all, he learned to change into different animals.

mountain a big hill

fruit you get this sweet thing from trees and can eat it; bananas and apples are different fruits

rock a very big stone

monkey an animal that eats fruit, lives in trees, and usually has a long tail

fight (*past* **fought**) to hit someone many times; when you hit someone many times

strong with a body that works well

king the most important man in a country

holy we use this word about a place, person, or thing that is near to god or heaven

cloud a big white or black thing in the sky; rain comes from it

magic unusual and making things happen in a way that you can't understand

word a thing that you say or write

After a long time, Monkey thanked the holy man and left. He got on his cloud, and went back to the Mountain of Fruit and Flowers. He soon met one of the monkeys there. 'Remember me?' said Monkey. 'I'm your king.'

'But a red **demon** is now our king,' said the monkey.

'Ha! I can soon stop that!' cried Monkey. He took out some of his hairs and said magic words over them. They changed into hundreds of little monkeys. At once, these little monkeys went up the mountain, and fought the red demon. The demon ran away.

'This time, there was one demon,' said Monkey. 'But what can I do next time – when more demons come?'

'I know,' said one old monkey. 'Go to the **Dragon** King of the **Ocean** in the East, and speak to him. He knows everything about fighting demons.'

So Monkey got on his cloud, went to the Ocean in the East, and spoke to the Dragon King. The Dragon King knew of Monkey and was afraid of him. So he helped him.

'You need these,' said the Dragon King. And he gave Monkey some **armour**, and a very long **staff**.

'I can't carry that staff!' cried Monkey.

'Yes, you can. Watch this,' said the Dragon King, and he cried, 'Change!' Suddenly the staff was very little.

'Thank you! You're right! I can carry it, behind my ear!' said Monkey. And he put the little staff behind his ear, and went home.

Far up in the sky, the **Emperor** of **Heaven** looked down through the clouds.

'Hmm. We need to watch carefully,' he said to the **Moon Goddess**. 'Monkey can do many different things now.' So the Emperor asked Monkey up to Heaven.

demon a very bad person

dragon a big animal that can fly through the sky; they bring good luck in China; fire dragons have fire in them; water dragons live in water

ocean a big sea

armour when you wear this, people cannot kill you

staff a long, thin piece of wood that you use for fighting

emperor the most important man in a number of countries

heaven where gods live; good people go here after they die

moon this is in the sky at night and it gives light

goddess a female being who never dies, and who decides what happens in the world

'You can work here with my horses,' the Emperor told Monkey when he arrived.

'Thank you,' said Monkey happily.

But one day, the Dragon **Prince** of Heaven spoke to his brother. And Monkey heard them. 'Monkey is doing the dirtiest work in Heaven!' laughed the Dragon Prince. 'He never stops taking horse **muck** to the Emperor's gardens!'

'Grrr!' thought Monkey angrily. He ran to the Emperor of Heaven's home. All the most important people in Heaven were there. 'Why am I doing the worst work in Heaven?' asked Monkey in front of everybody.

'Who is this?' asked the big, fat **Admiral** of Heaven.

'Yes, go back to the horses at once,' said the tall, thin **General** of Heaven.

But Monkey stood angrily in front of the Emperor, and didn't move.

'Please find some more interesting work for Monkey,' smiled the Moon Goddess. She felt sorry for Monkey.

In the end, the Emperor told Monkey, 'Very well. Go and work in my **peach** garden. But you need to watch the peaches there carefully. Nobody must eat them. Because after people eat those peaches, they're **immortal**.'

prince the son of a king or emperor

muck this is dirty, and it comes from animals

admiral a very important officer with a big ship who tells sailors what to do

general a very important officer in the army who tells soldiers what to do

peach (plural **peaches**) this big, round, yellow fruit has a hard stone in the middle

immortal never dying

3

So Monkey went to the peach garden. He sat under one of the trees, and slept in the warm sun. When he opened his eyes, he felt hungry.

'Mmm, I'd like one of those nice peaches,' he thought, and he took a big peach from the tree and ate it.

'That was wonderful!' he said. So he took one more. Soon, there was only one last peach in the garden.

'Monkey! Come here!' cried the Emperor the next morning. 'Did you eat my peaches yesterday?'

'Yes,' said Monkey. 'They were very nice, thank you. And now I'm immortal.'

'Oh no!' cried the Emperor. 'What can I do with him?' he asked everybody.

'Put him in your **oven**,' said the Admiral of Heaven. 'And leave him there for forty-nine days.'

'Yes!' said the General of Heaven. 'Nobody can come out of that alive!'

oven this is hot, it has a door, and you melt or burn things in it

So the Emperor put Monkey in the oven at once.

After forty-nine days, the Emperor opened the oven

doors. 'Monkey is dead by now, I think,' he said.

But Monkey quickly came out. He now had red eyes, and a very strong body.

'Ha! I'm immortal. You forgot that,' said Monkey. 'And I've got new eyes! I can see demons with them. Look, there are some demons on that mountain down under the clouds!'

'Oh no!' cried the Admiral of Heaven. 'He's quicker and stronger than before!'

'Then there's only one answer,' said the Emperor. 'Monkey, you must leave Heaven at once.'

'What?!' said Monkey. 'Go back down to **Earth**?!'

'Yes. After all, you ate my peaches,' cried the Emperor. 'But that's not everything. I'm going to put you under a mountain for five hundred years. And I'm going to put my **seal** on the mountain, so you can't get out and run away.'

'But how am I going to eat and drink?' asked Monkey.

'You can have a helper. He can visit you every day,' answered the Emperor. 'Goodbye, Monkey!'

Nearly five hundred years went past. Then, one day, **Buddha** visited a holy woman in China. She was called **Guanyin**. 'Guanyin,' said Buddha. 'I'm afraid for the people of China. They think more of Earth than of Heaven.'

'That's true,' answered Guanyin.

'In India, there are many holy **writings**,' said Buddha. 'These can help. You must find a young Chinese **monk**. He must go to India and bring back those holy writings.'

'Very well,' said Guanyin.

So Guanyin visited an old Chinese **monastery**, and she found a young monk there. He was called **Tripitaka**.

'I need your help,' said Guanyin. 'You must go to India and bring back some holy writings to China.'

Tripitaka listened carefully. 'The road is going to be long,' said Guanyin. 'And there are many mountains, rivers, and angry demons between here and India.'

The young monk looked at his feet.

'So, Tripitaka, can you go to the west for me – and for Buddha?' asked Guanyin.

Earth we live on this

seal something with your name on that you put on a letter or door; when people want to open the letter or door, they must break this

Buddha /'bʊdə/

Guanyin /gwʌn'jɪn/

writings important written words

monk a man who wants to do Heaven's work on Earth, and who lives very simply

monastery a building where holy men live and work away from the world

Tripitaka /ˌtrɪpɪ'tækə/

5

READING CHECK

Match the first and second parts of the sentences.

a	Monkey is born from	**1**	a red demon.
b	Soon, Monkey is king of all the	**2**	an old rock.
c	Monkey learns a lot of things from	**3**	Monkey.
d	Hundreds of little monkeys fight	**4**	horses.
e	The Dragon King gives Monkey	**5**	monkeys.
f	Monkey works with the Emperor's	**6**	a holy man.
g	The Moon Goddess feels sorry for	**7**	a mountain.
h	Monkey eats all the Emperor's	**8**	a young monk.
i	The Emperor puts Monkey under	**9**	a staff.
j	Guanyin finds, and speaks to	**10**	peaches.

WORD WORK

1 Match the words with the pictures.

a	fruit 2	**e**	demon ☐	**i**	peach ☐
b	Earth ☐	**f**	staff ☐	**j**	monastery ☐
c	seal ☐	**g**	writings ☐	**k**	dragon ☐
d	monkey ☐	**h**	rock ☐	**l**	monk ☐

2 Find new words from Chapter 1 to complete the sentences.

a When you f i g h t demons, you must wear a _ _ _ _ _.

b An a _ _ _ _ _ _ _ knows all about ships, and a g _ _ _ _ _ _ knows all about fighting.

c Be careful! Don't walk in that horse m _ _ _ in front of you.

d Monkey is s _ _ _ _ _. He can run up a tall m _ _ _ _ _ _ _ _ _ very fast.

e The water in the o _ _ _ _ is dark today, and there are black c _ _ _ _ _ in the sky.

f A monk is a h _ _ _ man. He usually lives in a monastery.

g Cook the bread in the o _ _ _ for 50 minutes.

h The Emperor of Heaven never dies. He's i _ _ _ _ _ _ _ _.

i When the Dragon King says the w _ _ _ 'change', the big staff is suddenly very little. It's
m _ _ _ _!

j 'Does your country have a k _ _ _?' 'Yes, and his son is a p _ _ _ _ _.'

GUESS WHAT

What happens in the next chapter? Read the sentences and tick one box.

Tripitaka…

a ☐ says, 'No, thank you. I
don't want to go to India.'

b ☐ takes the road to the
west, but a demon kills him.

c ☐ begins to go to India on
a beautiful horse, and soon
meets Monkey.

CHAPTER TWO

A horse and a headband

The young monk Tripitaka looked at the holy woman Guanyin. 'Of course I can go on this **journey** to the west,' he said. 'But how can I fight against demons and go across rivers when there's only me?'

'You're going to have helpers,' said Guanyin.

'Where are they?' asked Tripitaka.

'You're going to meet them on the journey,' said Guanyin. 'I'm sorry, but I can't tell you any more.'

'And do I need to walk to India?' asked Tripitaka.

'Oh, no. I have a horse for you,' smiled Guanyin, and she brought a beautiful white horse from behind a tree. 'And here's one more thing,' said the holy woman, and she gave a beautiful **headband** to Tripitaka.

'What do I do with this?' he asked her.

'You put it on someone's head. Then, you say these holy words,' answered Guanyin, and she said the holy words.

journey when you go far; to go far

headband you wear this around your head

'The headband then **becomes** very **tight**. Of course, the wearer is going to listen very carefully to you after that.'

'Well, I'm not going to need the headband,' said Tripitaka. But he put it in his bag.

The next morning, Tripitaka got on his beautiful white horse. He left the monastery on the road to the West.

After a week, Tripitaka was on a road near a tall mountain when suddenly he heard some cries from behind a big, black rock. 'The **master's** coming! The master's coming!' the cries went.

Tripitaka began to feel afraid. Soon, he met a very old man with a bottle of water and a bag of fruit in his hands.

'What's all that noise?' Tripitaka asked.

'Those are the cries of Monkey,' said the old man. 'The Emperor of Heaven put him under that mountain five hundred years ago. I give him something to eat and drink every day. My father, my grandfather, my grandfather's father, and his grandfather before him, did this for many years before me. Monkey is waiting for someone, I think.'

Tripitaka went to the mountain, and he spoke to Monkey. 'I'm Tripitaka, the monk. You can go free. But you must become my helper, and come to India with me. We're going to find some holy writings there.'

'Oh, so you're my master!' Monkey said excitedly. 'The holy woman Guanyin came and spoke to me about you. I need to go on the journey to the west, and say 'sorry' for taking those peaches from the Emperor of Heaven's garden. Take the Emperor's seal off this mountain. Then I can get out of this rock.'

So Tripitaka took off the Emperor's seal. Monkey **jumped** out of the black rock. 'Wow! I'm free – after five hundred years!' he cried happily, and he began to run away.

become (*past* **became**) to begin to be

tight little for the wearer of it

master you call the man that you work for this

jump to move suddenly from one place to a different place

'Monkey! Come back!' said Tripitaka. 'I have something for you.' And he took the headband out of his bag.

'What's that?' Monkey asked, and he ran back.

'It's a wonderful headband,' Tripitaka said. 'When you wear it, you can suddenly understand many things!'

'Really?' said Monkey. 'I must put it on at once!'

He took the headband, and he put it on his head.

Tripitaka said the holy words. The headband suddenly became very tight. Monkey began jumping up and down.

'Stop! Stop!' he cried again and again. But the headband became tighter and tighter. 'I never want to run away again!' cried Monkey. 'I'm going to be your true helper, and journey to India and back with you.' Tripitaka stopped saying the holy words, and Monkey began to feel better.

'Thank you, Master,' he said to the young monk. 'Please don't do that again. Can I take the headband off now?'

'No, you must wear it all the time,' Tripitaka said. 'With that on your head, you're not going to run away again.'

So Tripitaka, the white horse, and Monkey began their journey. They **travelled** across dark mountains, and past big rocks, on the long road to India. Tripitaka sat on his horse, and Monkey walked carefully in front. He moved his eyes quickly from left to right. He looked for demons and **monsters** behind every rock and tree.

Early one morning, they arrived at a big river. The water in it was cold, and it ran past very quickly.

Tripitaka got off his horse. 'How are we going to go across this, Monkey?' Tripitaka asked tiredly.

'Hmm,' said Monkey. 'I need to think about that for a minute, Master.'

So Tripitaka and the horse waited next to the river.

Suddenly, a blue water dragon with big, angry eyes

travel to go to different places

monster a person or animal that is very bad to look at, and does very bad things

jumped out of the river. It took Tripitaka's horse in its long, white teeth, and it began to go down under the water. 'Stop!' Tripitaka cried. But the big river dragon was fast and strong. It carried the horse down under the water in its mouth.

Tripitaka sat down at the **side** of the river, and he put his head in his hands. 'How can I journey to India and back without a horse?' he cried. 'And what is the holy woman Guanyin going to say when she learns about this?'

side the left or right of something

ACTIVITIES

READING CHECK

Correct the mistake in each sentence.

a Guanyin gives a magic ~~bag~~ *headband* to Tripitaka.

b Tripitaka hears some cries from behind a big black tree.

c On the road, Tripitaka talks to a very old woman.

d Monkey ate all the apples in heaven, so he must go with Tripitaka.

e After nearly four hundred years, Monkey is free.

f Monkey must wear the headband some of the time.

g Monkey walks behind Tripitaka on the journey.

h On the road, Monkey moves his ears from left to right.

i One day, Monkey and Tripitaka come to a big ocean.

j A river dragon suddenly eats Tripitaka's dinner.

WORD WORK

Find eight more new words from Chapter 2 in the wordsquare.

J	O	U	R	N	E	Y	W	H
X	K	V	U	T	Z	P	M	E
M	B	E	C	O	M	E	A	A
O	S	Q	D	J	H	Y	S	D
N	T	R	A	V	E	L	T	B
S	S	Z	B	W	O	S	E	A
T	I	H	K	L	X	Q	R	N
E	D	P	T	I	G	H	T	D
R	E	J	U	M	P	H	Y	V

2 **Use the words from Activity 1 to complete these sentences.**

a This summer I want to ..... _travel_ .... to France and visit friends there.

b We're tired after our long . . . . here.

c That dog's very good. It always listens to its . . . .

d Hey! There's a . . . . with two heads and three eyes over there!

e Let's sit on this . . . . of the garden. It's nicer here.

f She'd like to . . . . a doctor when she's older.

g Don't . . . . down from that rock! Come down slowly.

h I don't like these shoes. They're very . . . . on my feet.

i He always wears a white . . . . when he plays tennis.

GUESS WHAT

What happens in the next chapter? Tick the boxes.

a Tripitaka begins the journey again on…

1 ☐ Monkey's back. **2** ☐ foot. **3** ☐ a new horse.

b The travellers go across the river on…

1 ☐ a small ship. **2** ☐ Monkey's staff. **3** ☐ a river dragon's back.

c Later on the journey, a monster…

1 ☐ fights Monkey. **2** ☐ eats Monkey. **3** ☐ runs away with Tripitaka.

CHAPTER THREE
The dragon prince and the monster

'I can help you, Master,' Monkey told Tripitaka.

He began calling the river dragon.

'Dragon! Where are you?' he cried. 'I want to talk to you.'

Soon the river dragon put its head out of the water.

'What do you want?' asked the dragon.

Just then, Monkey took the little staff from behind his ear and cried, 'Change!' The staff became very big, and he quickly began hitting the dragon over the head with it.

'You ate my master's horse!' he cried angrily. 'So take that... and that... and that!' The strong river dragon soon went under the water again.

Suddenly, the holy woman Guanyin was with them.

'Wait! Put down that staff, Monkey, and listen,' she said.

Monkey put the little staff behind his ear.

'Thank you,' smiled Guanyin. Then she told Tripitaka, 'That isn't a true river dragon. He's the Dragon Prince of Heaven. The Emperor put him here because he once said bad things to the Emperor's mother. The Prince cannot go back to Heaven before he carries a monk to India.'

'And I'm that monk!' said Tripitaka excitedly.

Suddenly, the dragon's head came out of the water again.

'Are you talking about me?' the dragon asked.

'Yes, Dragon Prince,' Guanyin said. 'But you forgot my words to you. You didn't tell this young monk your story when you first saw him. Why?' she asked angrily.

'I was very hungry,' answered the dragon. 'So I ate his horse first. My last dinner was weeks ago, you know.'

'Well, now you can be Tripitaka's new horse,' said Guanyin. At once, she changed the dragon into a beautiful, white horse. It went and stood near Tripitaka. 'Have a good journey!' cried Guanyin, before she suddenly left.

The three travellers stood near the river. They looked up and down it, but could see no ships. Its cold water **flowed** past very quickly. 'Well, we can't take a ship across, and we can't walk across,' said Tripitaka.

'Wait and see!' cried Monkey, and he took the little staff from behind his ear. 'Change,' he cried, and the staff became very big and long. Monkey put the long staff across the river, Then he, Tripitaka, and the white horse walked over it, from this side of the river to that side.

Once they were over, Monkey cried, 'Change!' The staff became little once more, and Monkey put it back behind his ear. 'Thanks, Monkey!' said Tripitaka, and Monkey smiled.

The next evening, the travellers were on the road when they saw a **farm**. 'It's late,' Tripitaka said. 'And we need beds for the night. Let's ask the farmer.'

Near the farm, they met the farmer's son, **Kao Tsai**.

'Can we stay here?' Tripitaka asked.

'No, sorry,' Kao Tsai answered. 'A monster lives in one of our farm buildings. We can't have visitors.'

flow to move one way

farm a house with land in the country

Kao Tsai /ˌkaʊ ˈtsaɪ/

15

'A monster?' asked Monkey. 'Is that true?'

'Yes. It's a **terrible** story,' Kao Tsai said.

'Three years ago, a young man came to work for my father, old Mr Kao. He was a good, strong worker, and at first everything went well. He often had dinner with us. He loved eating. And he became a friend to my sister. Her name's Blue **Orchid**.

'But after some months, this man began to change. His teeth became bigger, his eyes became angrier, and his hair became longer. His legs and arms became stronger, too.

'One morning, he came to the house. When we opened the door, we suddenly understood all those changes. Our farm worker was now a monster! He ran away, but the next day, we couldn't find my sister. We called her again and again. After many hours, I heard a noise from one of the little buildings next to our farm. I called through the door, "Blue Orchid, is that you?" And I heard my sister call back, "Yes! It's me. But now I'm the monster's **prisoner**, and I can't come out."

'This all happened six months ago. We don't see Blue Orchid now. We're afraid of that terrible monster, so we don't go near the building. What can we do?'

'You need me to help you!' Monkey cried, and he took out the staff from behind his ear. 'Now where's your sister?' he asked Kao Tsai, and they walked to the little farm building.

'Be careful,' said Kao Tsai. 'There's a lot of muck on the **ground** here.'

'Well, it is a farm after all,' laughed Monkey.

'Blue Orchid!' Kao Tsai called. 'There's someone here. His name's "Monkey", and he can help you.'

Blue Orchid slowly opened the door. 'The monster isn't here now,' she said. 'He usually comes at night.'

terrible very bad; making people afraid

orchid a plant with beautiful, colourful flowers that are unusual shapes

prisoner a person who is not free

ground we walk on this

'Quick, Blue Orchid. Run to the farm with your brother,' said Monkey. 'I'm going to wait here.'

Monkey went in, and waited quietly behind the door with his big staff. The monster came in late that evening. And Monkey jumped on his back, and hit him on the head with the staff.

'Ouch!' cried the monster. Then he moved, and Monkey **fell** to the ground without his staff. The monster stood over Monkey, and looked down at him. Monkey looked up, and saw a long muck **rake** in the monster's hand

'I'm going to kill you!' cried the monster angrily, and he brought the muck rake down on Monkey's head.

fall (*past* **fell**) to go down suddenly

rake this is long; you can move leaves or muck on the ground in a garden with it

READING CHECK

Are these sentences true or false? Tick the boxes.

		True	False
a	Monkey hits the river dragon with his staff.	☑	☐
b	The river dragon was once the Emperor of Heaven.	☐	☐
c	The river dragon becomes Tripitaka's new horse.	☐	☐
d	The travellers come to a monastery, and meet Kao Tsai there.	☐	☐
e	Kao Tsai tells the travellers about a monster.	☐	☐
f	The monster was once a good farm worker.	☐	☐
g	Kao Tsai's wife, Blue Orchid, is now the monster's prisoner.	☐	☐
h	Monkey wants to help Blue Orchid.	☐	☐
i	The monster has a fight with Tripitaka.	☐	☐
j	The monster wants to kill Monkey with a big staff.	☐	☐

WORD WORK

1 Complete the dialogues on page 19 with the words in the dragon.

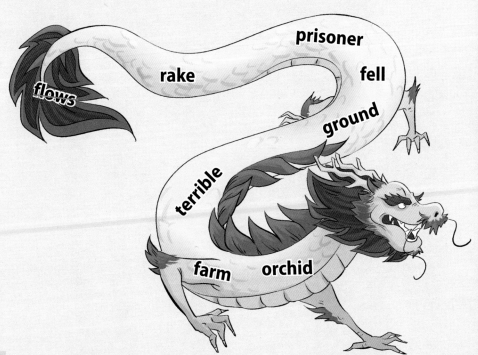

prisoner

rake

fell

flows

ground

terrible

farm   orchid

18

a 'Can we swim in the river?''No. It ......*flows*..... very fast here.'

b 'Where do you live?''On a .... in the country.'

c 'What are you afraid of?''The .... monster in this film!'

d 'How did you break your arm?''I .... off my bike.'

e 'Why is that man happy?''He was a ...., but now he's free.'

f 'What's this beautiful flower?''It's an ....'

g 'I'm going to work in the garden.''Do you want the .... ?'

h 'Where's my bus ticket?''On the .... near your foot.'

GUESS WHAT

What happens in the next chapter? Tick the boxes.

a When the monster hits Monkey …

1 ☐ Monkey begins to cry.

2 ☐ Monkey quickly jumps up again.

b Monkey learns more about the monster. He was once …

1 ☐ the Admiral of Heaven.

2 ☐ the Gardener of Heaven.

c Tripitaka, Monkey, and the monster meet …

1 ☐ a second monster in a river.

2 ☐ the Moon Goddess on a hill.

CHAPTER FOUR
The man-eating river-monster

The monster hit Monkey on the head with his muck rake. For a second, Monkey didn't move. Then he suddenly jumped up. 'Ha! You can't kill Monkey with your muck rake!' he cried. 'The Emperor of Heaven once put me in a big oven for forty-nine days. Now my body is wonderfully strong, and I'm immortal.'

The monster looked carefully at Monkey's face.

'I remember you,' said the monster slowly. 'You ate all the peaches in the Emperor's Peach Garden. I was the Admiral of Heaven then.'

'Ah, yes. I remember you! But what are you doing down here on Earth?' asked Monkey.

'It's a long story,' the monster said. 'The Emperor was angry with me because I became very good friends with the Moon Goddess. So I was born again here on Earth in this monster's body.'

'Well, I'm on a journey to India now,' said Monkey. 'I need to say 'sorry' for eating all the Emperor of Heaven's peaches. I'm travelling with a monk on a white horse.'

'What's that? A monk on a white horse?' cried the monster. 'Take me to him at once. Guanyin visited me, and I know all about your journey. I need to go to India and say 'sorry' about the Moon Goddess. And for not being nice to Blue Orchid when she was my prisoner.'

So the monster went with Tripitaka, Monkey, and the horse on their journey to India. They called him 'Pigsy'. When they all sat down for dinner that evening, Pigsy quickly ate everybody's **food**.

food you eat this

'Stop that!' cried Tripitaka. 'We need to eat too!'

'I'm sorry. I forgot,' said Pigsy, with a red face 'Every time I see a lot of food, I want to eat it all.'

Some days later, the travellers came to a big river – the River of the Flowing **Sand**. They felt tired after the day's journey, and they all sat down quietly with their backs to the river. Suddenly, there was a terrible noise from the water. The travellers quickly looked behind them. 'Ugh!' cried Tripitaka. 'What a terrible thing!'

sand it is yellow, and we find a lot of it on the beach

spade this is long; you can make holes in the ground in a garden with it

From the water, an angry monster looked at them. It had green eyes and yellow teeth, and it was very tall. In one of its thin arms there was a long **spade**, and it had a big water bottle at its side.

'Stand back everybody! It's a man-eater!' cried Pigsy. 'But I'm ready with my muck rake!'

Pigsy hit the river-monster over the head. But Monkey wanted to fight, too. He took out his staff, and hit the monster with it. River water went all over Tripitaka.

'Stop!' cried Tripitaka. 'I don't like fighting. You know that.'

Pigsy stopped at once, but Monkey didn't stop hitting the river-monster angrily. So in the end, Tripitaka said the holy words. The headband at once became very tight on Monkey's head, and he stopped fighting, too.

The monster moved away and went under the water. Tripitaka began walking up and down.

'How are we going to go across the river with that monster in it?' he said.

'Without fighting, who knows?' said Monkey angrily, and he walked away. But Pigsy stood next to Tripitaka.

'It's all right, Master,' Pigsy said. 'I can help you.'

He jumped into the water. Then he went and found the monster on a big rock in the river.

'Wait! Don't hit me! I wasn't always a monster,' the monster told Pigsy. 'I was once the General of Heaven.'

'I remember you!' cried Pigsy. 'I was once the Admiral of Heaven! What are you doing here on Earth?'

'I broke the Emperor of Heaven's most expensive **vase**,' said the monster. 'So I was born again here in the River of the Flowing Sand. My name's Sandy now.'

Pigsy looked carefully at Sandy. 'Don't tell me,' he said. 'You want to go with a young monk and his helpers on a journey to India?'

'That's right!' Sandy answered excitedly. 'Guanyin spoke to me. I must make the journey to India and say 'sorry' because I broke that beautiful vase.'

Pigsy took Sandy to Tripitaka. Sandy sat on the ground in front of the young monk. 'Master, how can I begin to help you on your long and important journey?' he asked.

'Take us across the river,' answered Tripitaka.

'Watch this!' said Sandy. He quickly took his big water-bottle in his hands, and he made a ship from it. 'Jump in everybody!' cried Sandy. So they all went happily across the river in Sandy's water-bottle ship.

After that, the travellers journeyed for days. Monkey walked in front – always ready for demons and monsters.

vase you put flowers in this

Next, there was Tripitaka on his white horse. Sandy came after Tripitaka, with his long spade in his hand. Last of all, there was Pigsy. He carried many of the travellers' things, and his muck rake, too. They went through old villages, past little farms, and over cold mountains.

One night, the travellers stopped at a monastery. Tripitaka was tired after a long day, and he went to bed early. He closed his eyes, and he soon slept. In his sleep, the young monk saw in front of him an old man with a terrible white face. There was water all over his hair and body. He came nearer. 'Oh, I am a king without a **kingdom**!' he cried. 'Please help me, Tripitaka!

kingdom the country of a king

READING CHECK

Choose the correct words to complete these sentences.

a The monster *remembers* / *doesn't remember* Monkey.

b The monster was once an important man in *India* / *heaven*.

c The travellers give a new *horse* / *name* to the monster.

d At dinner, Pigsy *drinks all the water* / *eats all the food*.

e Monkey and Pigsy begin to *fight* / *run after* the river monster.

f The river monster once lived in *heaven* / *the ocean*.

g Then he broke the Emperor's *water bottle* / *vase*.

h The river monster is called *Sandy* / *Guanyin*.

i The river monster makes a ship from his *spade* / *water bottle*.

j When they are over the river, the travellers visit a *farm* / *monastery*.

k Tripitaka sees an old *woman* / *man* in his sleep one night.

WORD WORK

1 Use the letters in the water bottles to make new words from Chapter 4.

a .....spade.....   b ....

c ....   d ....   e ....

2 Use the words from Activity 1 to answer these questions.

a What can you take muck from the ground with?

..... spade ..... .

b What do we call a country with a king?

....

c What is yellow, and is often near the sea?

....

d What can you put flowers in?

....

e What do you have at breakfast or dinner time?

....

GUESS WHAT

Tripitaka sees a king in his sleep. What is this king's story? Tick three sentences.

a ☐ He had a kingdom near the monastery.

b ☐ He had a kingdom in India.

c ☐ A terrible demon killed him, and took all his money.

d ☐ A very bad man took his kingdom by magic.

e ☐ He wants his kingdom back, and he needs Tripitaka's help.

f ☐ He wants his money back, and he needs Tripitaka's help.

CHAPTER FIVE
The king in the well

'I once was the King of Cockadoodle,' the old man told Tripitaka in his sleep. 'That's a kingdom near here.'

And he began to tell Tripitaka his story.

'Five years ago, there was no water in my country. It never rained, and the farmers stopped bringing food into the towns. The people were hungry, and I needed to do something quickly. Then, one day, a **magician** arrived. He could make clouds in the sky. The weather changed, and soon it rained every day. The farms were green again, and the people were happy. I told the magician, "Please stay. My kingdom is nothing without you." In the end, he said "yes", and I gave him a house.

magician
somebody that makes things happen in a way that you don't understand

'But early one morning, I was at the **well** in the **palace** garden when I heard someone behind me. It was the magician. He hit me, and I fell down the well. Then he said some magic words. When I looked up, I could see his face far away. But it wasn't his face, it was my face. The magician was now me, and I could do nothing about it!

'The **imposter** put an apple tree over the well, and he went to live in the palace with my family. He is now the King of Cockadoodle. And nobody knows the true story.'

Tripitaka moved in his sleep. 'How can I help?' he asked.

'You must take this green **ring** with my seal on it,' answered the king. 'Give it to my son, the prince. When he sees it, he's going to understand.'

The next morning, Tripitaka opened his eyes in bed at the monastery. He saw the green ring in his hand, and he told Monkey about the King of Cockadoodle.

'Leave everything to me, Master!' said Monkey. 'I can help the king, and drive away that imposter.'

Monkey soon learned something interesting. At ten o'clock the next day, the Prince of Cockadoodle and his men wanted to visit the country near the monastery on their horses.

The next morning, Monkey jumped on his white cloud. He looked for the prince and his men, and found them not far from the monastery. Monkey quickly changed into a big fat bird, and ran in front of the horses. The prince suddenly saw the bird and thought, 'Wow! I want to eat that for my dinner.' So he took a long **arrow** from his bag.

The arrow went up through the sky, and it hit the big, fat bird. Monkey, in the bird's body, went quickly across the sky to the monastery. Then he changed back into Monkey, and put the arrow into the monastery door. Monkey then

well a place where you can get water from under the ground

palace a big house where a king, an emperor, or an important person lives

imposter someone who says that they are something which they are not

ring a circle of metal that that you wear on a finger

arrow you shoot things with this

went into the monastery, and jumped into a box there.

The prince went after the bird on his horse, with all his men behind him. He soon arrived at the monastery, and he found the arrow in the monastery door. 'What's my arrow doing there?' he said. He took the arrow out of the door, and walked into the building. But Tripitaka stood in front of him. 'Move!' cried the prince angrily.

'I'm a holy monk! You can't say "move" to me!' answered Tripitaka.

'Well, I'm the Prince of Cockadoodle, and people always listen to me,' the prince cried. 'Take that monk away!' he said to his men.

But Monkey opened the box, and came out. He said some magic words, and suddenly nobody could move for a minute. 'Prince!' said Monkey. 'We have something interesting for you.' Then he took the green seal ring from Tripitaka's hand, and gave it to the prince.

'That's my father's ring!' the prince said.

'Take it,' Monkey said. 'And close your eyes.'

The prince took the ring in his hand, and closed his eyes. After some minutes, he opened his eyes again. 'I saw my father!' he cried. 'And he told me something terrible. The king in the palace is an imposter, he said. Is it true?'

'Yes,' answered Monkey.

'But what can I do about this?' the prince cried.

'You must wait,' said Monkey. 'We are going to help your father.' So the prince waited at the monastery.

Later that day, Monkey spoke to Pigsy. 'I need your help tonight,' said Monkey.

'Sorry, I'm feeling tired,' answered Pigsy.

'Please help me, Pigsy,' said Monkey. 'Then you can have some **treasure**.'

treasure
something expensive, like gold or jewels

'Mmm,' thought Pigsy. 'Is that "treasure" going to be some nice food?'

'All right. I can help you,' he told Monkey.

That night, they went to the palace garden. Pigsy broke open the **gate** with his long muck rake. Then they went in, and found the apple tree. 'The treasure is under that tree, Pigsy,' said Monkey. So Pigsy opened his big mouth, and he took away the tree in his teeth.

'Oh look! There's a well under the tree!' cried Pigsy.

'Yes, the treasure is down the well,' said Monkey.

'Shall I go down there and have a look?' asked Pigsy excitedly.

'Yes,' said Monkey.

So Pigsy went down the well. He found something in the dark well water. 'This is the treasure!' Pigsy thought, and he carried it up to Monkey.

Pigsy put the thing on the ground at Monkey's feet, and then he looked at it. 'Yuk!' he said suddenly. 'That's not treasure. It's a dead body!'

'That's right,' said Monkey. 'It's the body of the true King of Cockadoodle.'

gate a big door

29

'And you knew that all the time!' cried Pigsy angrily.

'Well... yes,' smiled Monkey. 'But I needed your help because you're very strong.'

'I see,' said Pigsy. 'And now, don't tell me: I need to carry that body back to the monastery, too.'

'No, that's all right,' said Monkey. 'I can do that.'

Monkey quickly took out some of his hairs, and said some magic words. Hundreds of little monkeys ran to the dead body, and they carried it back to the monastery. The prince was there, with Tripitaka and Sandy.

At the monastery, the prince looked at his father's body.

'This is terrible,' he cried. 'My father is dead, and that imposter is now king.'

'Wait here!' said Monkey. 'I need to ask for help from some of my friends in Heaven.'

Monkey jumped on his cloud, went up to Heaven, and spoke to the Moon Goddess.

'Here, have this magic peach drink,' she said. 'It comes from the fruit in the Peach Garden of Heaven. When someone drinks it, they become immortal.'

Monkey took the bottle, came back to Earth, and gave the magic peach drink to the king. The king slowly opened his eyes and looked at Tripitaka.

'Thank you, holy monk,' he said.

'Don't thank me,' answered Tripitaka. 'Thank Monkey.'

'And me,' Pigsy said. 'I helped, too!'

'Let's all go to the palace tomorrow,' Monkey said. 'Then we can talk to that imposter.'

Tripitaka, Monkey, Pigsy and Sandy took the true king to the palace the next day.

He wore a big hat on his head, and nobody could see his face. At the palace door, Tripitaka spoke to one of the king's men. In the end, the travellers went in, and saw the imposter king. He looked down at the travellers, and said, 'Who are you? And what are you doing in my kingdom?'

'We're four travellers on a long journey to India,' said Tripitaka. 'We're going to bring back holy writings.'

'Oh!' said the imposter. 'But who's that fifth man in the big hat behind you?'

'He's a man with a terrible story,' said Sandy. 'Long ago, he was a king, but there was no rain in his kingdom, and his people were hungry. Then, one day, a magician arrived, and made a rain cloud–'

'You dirty monster,' cried the imposter, 'stop there!'

Just then, the true king took off his hat. 'You're not the King of Cockadoodle!' he told the imposter.

The imposter stood up angrily. He said some magic words, made a big, black cloud in the sky, and jumped on it.

'All right. So I'm not the King of Cockadoodle,' he laughed coldly. 'But you're never going to take me alive!' And with that, he left on the black cloud.

ACTIVITIES

READING CHECK

Put the sentences in order. Number them 1-11.

a ☐ Monkey becomes a big bird, and he flies to the monastery.
b ☐ The king tells Tripitaka his story, and gives a ring to him.
c ☐ Pigsy and Monkey go to the palace garden at night.
d ☐ Monkey wants to help. He finds the prince and his men.
e ☐ The travellers speak to the imposter. The imposter leaves.
f ☐ The prince closes his eyes, and learns about the imposter.
g ☐ The prince goes after the bird, and arrives at the monastery.
h ☐ Monkey gives a magic drink to the king.
i ☐ Pigsy goes down the well, and finds the king's dead body.
j ☐ At the monastery, Tripitaka gives the ring to the prince.
k ☐ The king drinks, and he becomes alive again.

WORD WORK

Use the pictures to write sentences with new words from Chapter 5.

a He isn't the true king. He's an

He isn't the true King. He's an imposter.

b The water in the village comes from an old

....

c You can go into the garden through the front

....

d She's wearing a _____ on her right hand.

....

32

e The king lives in a big

....

f There's under the ground here, people say.

....

g An suddenly hit the door.

....

h He can do magic. He's a

....

GUESS WHAT

What happens in the next chapter? Complete the sentences with the correct names.

| Buddha | Guanyin | Monkey | Pigsy | Sandy | Tripitaka |

a The travellers become tired and angry with . . . . He runs away.

b . . . . goes and looks for food, but he doesn't come back.

c Demons come and take . . . . and . . . . away.

d . . . . gives some holy writings to the travellers.

e . . . . makes a magic cloud for the travellers to travel home on.

CHAPTER SIX

The journey home

'Nobody runs away from me,' said Monkey. He jumped on his cloud, and soon came back with the imposter.

'Who are you?' cried the true king.

'Your dark side,' said the imposter.

'My dark side?' asked the king.

'Yes,' answered the imposter. 'Some years ago, you forgot your people, and became a bad king. The Emperor of Heaven saw this, and was angry. So he brought out your bad side – me.'

The king thought carefully. 'Hmm,' he said. 'Well, I'm sorry for that now.' Then the imposter walked into the true king, and was no longer there.

The king called his men. 'Let's thank these travellers. Bring food. We must have a big dinner tonight!'

'Yummy,' said Pigsy hungrily.

'No,' said Tripitaka. 'We can't stay any longer. We must travel west at once.'

'Without dinner?' cried Pigsy.

'Without dinner,' said Tripitaka.

'Very well,' said the king. He and the prince said goodbye to the travellers, and they left.

After many months, the road west became very bad. 'We're never going to arrive,' said Monkey angrily one evening. 'Oh, be quiet!' said Sandy.

'Yes,' said Pigsy. 'We're tired of listening to you, Monkey!'

The next morning, Tripitaka could not find Monkey.

'We can do without him,' said Tripitaka. 'Let's go.'

Nobody saw Monkey all day. Late that afternoon, the

three travellers arrived in a village. 'I'm going to look for food,' said Pigsy. He walked away. Sandy, Tripitaka, and the horse waited near the road. In the village, Pigsy walked past a big house. A beautiful young woman was at the gate. 'Can I help you, traveller?' she asked.

'Mmm. My name's Pigsy. I'm looking for food,' he smiled.

'My name's **Lotus** Flower,' said the young woman. 'My family likes to help travellers. Come and meet my father.'

'OK,' said Pigsy, and he went with her into the house.

Suddenly, Lotus Flower changed into a white demon. Then a blue demon in blue armour came in. He had a knife in his hand. 'This is my father,' the white demon laughed. 'We don't like to *help* travellers, we like to *eat* them!'

'Where's Pigsy?' Sandy asked Tripitaka some time later. 'Let's look for him!' They left the horse, and walked into the village. Suddenly they fell into a **trap**. Soon they saw the faces of two demons over them.

'Good,' laughed the demons. 'Your friend is ready for our dinner tomorrow. And now we're going to eat you, too!'

'Help!' cried Tripitaka. 'Where's Monkey?'

That night, Monkey heard Tripitaka's cries in his sleep.

'My master needs me!' he thought.

Early next morning, he jumped on his cloud, and travelled back along the road. At the village, he found Tripitaka's horse. With his quick, red eyes, he saw the demons. They were

lotus a water plant with a big beautiful flower

trap something that people make to catch somebody in

near an open oven, with long knives in their hands. Tripitaka, Pigsy and Sandy stood between them.

Monkey moved nearer. He said some magic words, and his cloud rained down on the oven. The demons looked up angrily, and Monkey jumped down with his staff. He hit the demons with it, and they ran away. Monkey looked at Tripitaka, Pigsy, and Sandy. They were tired and afraid.

'I left you,' said Monkey. 'I'm sorry.'

'Look, we're stronger when we're all here on the journey. I understand that now,' answered Tripitaka. 'We need you with us, Monkey.'

There are many more stories about the travellers' Journey to the West. They went across mountains, rivers, and oceans, fell into many traps, and fought many demons and monsters. But in the end, they arrived at the Holy Mountain in India – Buddha's home.

Tripitaka and his helpers went up to Buddha's holy palace. Tripitaka fell to the ground in front of Buddha. Monkey, Pigsy, Sandy, and the white horse waited behind him. 'We come from China,' said Tripitaka. 'We want to bring back some of your holy writings for our people.'

'Yes, Guanyin told me about you,' smiled Buddha. And he gave some beautiful **scrolls** to Tripitaka.

'Take these home with you,' he said.

'Thank you,' said Tripitaka, and they left.

But early on their journey home, Monkey looked at the scrolls.

'Hey, there isn't any writing on them!' he cried. So the travellers went back up the Holy Mountain and told Buddha.

'Ah! I wanted to **test** you,' smiled Buddha. 'But you did well in the test. These are the true scrolls.'

scroll a long piece of paper, often with writing on, that is rolled up for carrying

test to do something to someone to see what they do; when you do something to someone to see what they do

This time, he gave them scrolls with writing on them, and the travellers began their journey home again.

Soon after that, Guanyin visited Buddha in India.

'Those travellers had a long journey here,' she said. 'So I'm going to make a magic yellow cloud for them. It's going to take them back to China in eight days.'

Soon the travellers arrived home with the holy writings. They left these in a Chinese monastery. The scrolls helped the people of China to think more of Heaven, and to live better. Then the Emperor of Heaven took the travellers up to his kingdom over the clouds. They sat there in his palace.

'Thank you,' the Emperor told Monkey, Pigsy, Sandy and the white horse. 'You helped Tripitaka on his journey to India. You once did bad things, but these are all past. So now you can live in Heaven. Pigsy and the white horse, you can be **Altar** Boys. When food falls to the ground near any altars, you can eat it. Sandy, you can be Master of the Well of Heaven. And Tripitaka and Monkey, you can be Heaven's Helpers of Everyone on Earth.'

'Thank you, Holy Emperor!' they all cried.

altar a special high table in a temple

READING CHECK

Correct twelve more mistakes in the story.

goodbye

The travellers say 'hello' to the King of

Cockadoodle, and leave without breakfast.

Later, they all become angry with Monkey, and

he goes away. The next day, Tripitaka, Pigsy,

and Sandy arrive in a town, and Pigsy goes and

looks for treasure.

Pigsy meets Lotus Flower, a beautiful old

woman. Suddenly she becomes a green

demon. Just then, her brother – a blue demon – arrives.

Sandy and Tripitaka look for Pigsy, but they fall into a well, and the demons

find them. The next day, the demons want to eat Sandy, Tripitaka, and Pigsy.

But Monkey arrives on his white horse. He hits the demons, and they run away.

After some time, the travellers arrive at Guanyin's home in India. Buddha gives

some scrolls to them. But these scrolls have no pictures on them.

In the end, Buddha gives the true scrolls to them. Guanyin makes a magic

orange cloud for them. They go back to China on it in eighty days. The

Emperor of China takes them up to his kingdom in the clouds, and they live

there after that.

WORD WORK

1 Find four more new words from Chapter 6 in Monkey's cloud. Write the extra letters in order. They make a story character's name.

altargtrapuanscrollytestilotusn

The story character's name is _ _ _ _ _ _ _.

2 Match each word from activity 1 with a sentence, and show where it goes.

a I gave some flowers to my mother on her birthday......*lotus*.....

b Holy smoke went up from the in the monastery....................

c She opened the long and read the writing on it....................

d Teachers ask questions when they want to their students....................

e They fell into a big and they couldn't get out....................

GUESS WHAT

What do you think happens after the story ends? Tick the boxes.	Yes	No
a Monkey becomes good, and he never does bad things again.	☐	☐
b Monkey can never truly change, and he leaves heaven again.	☐	☐
c Pigsy feels happy in heaven because he has a lot of food there.	☐	☐
d Pigsy leaves heaven because he wants his muck rake.	☐	☐
e Sandy feels happy in heaven because he's working with water.	☐	☐
f Sandy visits Earth, and swims in his old river, every day.	☐	☐
g Tripitaka helps many people on Earth, and this pleases him.	☐	☐
h Tripitaka doesn't often see Monkey, Pigsy, or Sandy, so he feels bad.	☐	☐

Project A   *Famous quest stories*

A 'quest' is a journey to find something important.

1   Read the text, and complete the table.

The story of *Journey to the West* begins long ago in China. A young Buddhist monk, Tripitaka, goes on a journey with three travellers – Monkey, Pigsy and Sandy. They need to visit the home of Buddha, far away in India. The holy woman Guanyin helps them.

On this quest, the travellers need to find some Buddhist scrolls, and bring them back to China. On their journey, they go across fast-flowing rivers, and cold, dark mountains. They meet terrible river dragons, and angry demons, too.

In the end, the travellers arrive in India, and Buddha gives the holy scrolls to them. They take the scrolls back home to the people of China.

Journey to the West	
When and where does the story begin?	
Who goes on the quest?	
Where do they need to go?	
Who helps them?	
What do they need to find, and why?	
Which places do they travel through?	
What things or people do they meet?	
What happens in the end?	

2   Read the notes, and complete the text on page 41. Use a dictionary to help you.

Jason and the Golden Fleece	
When and where does the story begin?	*Many years ago, in Greece*
Who goes on the quest?	*Jason, the Argonauts*
Where do they need to go?	*The kingdom of Colchis*
Who helps them?	*The goddesses Hera, Athena, and Aphrodite*
What do they need to find?	*A golden fleece*
Which places do they travel through?	*Two big moving rocks – the Symplegades* *Different islands*
What things or people do they meet?	*Angry bird-women & earth-monsters with six arms*
What happens in the end?	*Get past a big dragon & take the golden fleece*

The story of . . . . begins . . . . in . . . . A young Greek man,
. . . ., goes on a journey to the kingdom of . . . .
He travels there by sea. His ship is the *Argo*, and Jason's friends on the ship
are . . . . The goddesses . . . . help them.
On his quest, Jason and his men need to find a . . . . Its . . . .
can help Jason to . . . . from his bad uncle, King Pelias.
On their journey, Jason and the Argonauts take the *Argo* between the
Symplegades – . . . . in the sea. They visit different . . . .,
too. There they meet . . . ., and . . . .
In the end, they arrive in Colchis. Jason must get past a big
. . . . to take . . . . He goes home to Greece
with it, and becomes king.

**3 Write about one of these quests, or a different quest story that you know.
Use a dictionary to help you.**

The Lord of the Rings

Frodo Baggins's quest to destroy
the One Ring.

King Arthur and the Knights of the Round Table

Sir Galahad's quest for the Holy Grail.

THE WONDERFUL WIZARD OF OZ

Dorothy's quest to go back home to Kansas.

Project B *A magazine story*

1 Read the magazine story below. Answer the questions.

a Who wrote it?

☐ Guanyin   ☐ Tripitaka   ☐ Sandy

☐ Monkey   ☐ Pigsy

b Which page and which lines of *Journey to the West* is it about? Page . . . . Lines . . . .

China Weekly Magazine: Reader's Story

I MET AN ANGRY RIVER-DRAGON
FACE-TO-FACE!

Last year, I was on a long journey to India when something truly terrible happened.

I was on the road with my friend one morning when we came to a big, fast-flowing river. 'How are we going to get across that?' I asked my friend. He sat down, and began to think.

I waited by the river with my horse, and gave some horse-food to him. He was a wonderful new horse with a beautiful white coat.

Well, suddenly there was a terrible noise, and a big monster came up out of the river at me. It was a blue river dragon with angry eyes, and long teeth! Before I could do a thing, the dragon took my horse in its teeth, and went down under the water. I cried, 'Stop! Stop!' again and again, but it didn't come back.

I later learned more about the dragon. It wasn't a real dragon at all. It was the Dragon Prince of Heaven!

I often think about that horse. He was my first horse, you see. I'm never going to forget that terrible morning when I lost him to the river-dragon.

Do you have an interesting story to tell our readers? Email it to: chinaweeklymagazine.com

2 Use the words in the box to write a magazine story by Monkey.

I WAS IN AN OVEN FOR FORTY-NINE DAYS
BUT I CAME OUT ALIVE!

Some years ago / was / when / in Heaven / interesting / I / happened / to me. / something

It / one day / I / all / began / did / something / when / very bad.

you see! / often I / bad or stupid things, do /

This time / angry / the Emperor's peaches / with me! / from his garden, / and / he / was / I / ate / truly

'Put that monkey / The Admiral of Heaven / at once!' / said / to / in your oven / the Emperor,

the Emperor / me / left me there / for forty-nine days! / So / put / and / in his oven,

red eyes. / I did not die. / hard body / When / I / I / had a / and / But / came out,

am the / demons, / I / can / now / monkey / I / strongest / in the / and / world! / see

forget / am not / changed / my life. / because / going to / I / that day / it

3 Read the magazine headlines. Match them with the story characters.

a
An imposter took my father's kingdom!

b
I was the prisoner of a terrible monster!

c
I broke the Emperor's vase!

d
The Emperor saw me with the Moon-Goddess!

e
Dad and I nearly ate three travellers for dinner!

1 Blue Orchid

2 Pigsy

3 The Prince of Cockadoodle

4 Lotus Flower

5 Sandy

4 Choose a headline from exercise 3. Write a magazine story by the *Journey to the West* character for that headline.

5 Put your magazine story on the classroom wall for your classmates to read.

6 Read your classmates' stories. Which is the funniest?

GRAMMAR

GRAMMAR CHECK

There is / are, There was / were affirmative and negative

We use there is (or there's) and there are to talk about things and people in a place. We use it for the present.

We use there's with singular nouns and there are with plural nouns. The negative form is There isn't / aren't.

There's a red demon.   *There aren't any peaches now.*

We use there was / wasn't and there were / weren't to talk about the past. We use there was with singular nouns and there were with plural nouns.

There wasn't any answer.   *There were four travellers.*

1 **Look at the picture. Complete the sentences with *there is, there are, there isn't*, or *there aren't*.**

a ....There..is... a big peach in Monkey's hand.

b .... a well in the garden.

c Behind Monkey, ... two peach trees.

d .... a smile on Monkey's face.

e .... any demons in the garden.

f In the sky, ... three clouds.

g .... a headband on Monkey's head.

2 **Complete the paragraph with *there was, there were, there wasn't*, or *there weren't*.**

Long ago, **a)** ...there..was... a mountain in China. On the mountain, **b)** .... any houses or people, but **c)** .... many monkeys – and **d)** .... a big, red rock. One morning, there **e)** .... a sudden noise. The red rock broke open, and a big, strong monkey came out. He was called Monkey. **f)** .... a stronger monkey on the mountain than Monkey, so he became the King of the Monkeys.

GRAMMAR CHECK

Linkers: *so* and *because*

We use so to link two sentences when the second sentence explains a result. We put a comma before the so part of the sentence.

We're afraid of that monster, so <u>we don't want to fight it</u>.
(= result of first part of sentence)

We use because to link two sentences when the second sentence explains a reason.

But I need your help because <u>you're very strong</u>.
(= reason for first part of sentence)

Because can go at the beginning of the sentence, too. We put a comma after the because part of the sentence when it comes first.

Because <u>after people eat those peaches</u>, they're immortal.
(= reason for second part of sentence)

---

3 Match the first and second parts of the sentences.

a	Tripitaka had a question,	**1**	because he was once bad.
b	Cries came from a rock	**2**	so he asked Guanyin.
c	Monkey was a prisoner	**3**	because he was now free.
d	Monkey was very happy	**4**	so Tripitaka felt afraid.
e	The headband was tight,	**5**	because the road was bad.
f	The journey went slowly	**6**	so Monkey cried, 'Stop!'

---

4 Complete the sentences with *so* or *because*.

a They couldn't go across the river, ...SO........ they stopped.

b Monkey needed to think, ... he sat down.

c They looked behind them .... they heard a noise.

d .... the river dragon was fast, they couldn't stop it.

e The river was big and cold, ... they didn't jump in.

f They felt angry .... the river dragon ate the horse.

g Tripitaka wasn't happy, ... he put his head in his hands.

GRAMMAR CHECK

Possessive adjectives and possessive 's

We use the possessive adjectives my, his, her, its, our, your, and their to show when something belongs to somebody, but we do not use a name or noun for the person.

Tripitaka's bag → his bag   *Guanyin's face → her face*

Different subjects have different possessive adjectives.

I → my   you → your   he → his   she → her

it → its   we → our   they → their

We use the possessive 's to show when something belongs to somebody, and we use a name or noun for the person. For singular nouns, we add 's.

Sandy's water bottle   the Emperor's peaches

5 Match the people with the things. Then write each phrase with the possessive 's.

a Mr Kao
b Tripitaka
c Monkey
d Kao Tsai
e Blue Orchid
f The monster

1 white horse
2 staff
3 cries
4 muck rake
5 farm
6 sister

a Mr Kao's farm.   **c** ....   **e** ....

b ....   **d** ....   **f** ....

6 Complete the sentences with the words in the box.

| her   his   ~~its~~   my   our   their   your |

a The dragon suddenly puts ......its...... head out of the water.

b 'Listen to Guanyin,' Tripitaka says. 'Hear .... story.'

c 'Go with the travellers on .... journey!' Guanyin says to the river dragon.

d 'Walk across the river on .... staff!' Monkey cries.

e 'Is this .... farm?' the travellers ask Kao Tsai.

f 'My sister and I live here,' he says. 'It's .... home.'

g 'The man changed into a monster,' says Kao Tsai. '................ teeth became bigger.'

GRAMMAR CHECK

Articles *a / an*, *the*

We use the indefinite article a / an when we talk about a singular noun, and it is not important which of many things we mean.

Monkey is born on a mountain in China.

We use a in front of a word that begins with a consonant sound, and an in front of a word that begins with a vowel sound.

Pigsy is a monster. That man is an imposter.

We use the definite article the when we talk about singular and plural nouns, and it is clear which of many things we mean.

One day, monkey leaves the mountain.
(= the Mountain of Fruit and Flowers.)

7 Complete these sentences with *a, an* or *the*.

a ....The......monster tells Monkey ....a........ long story.

b He was once .... Admiral of Heaven.

c But he became friends with .... Moon Goddess.

d 'I have .... exciting story, too!' Monkey says. 'I ate all

.... peaches in .... Emperor's garden. So

I needed to come down to Earth from .... sky.'

e 'Now I'm .... traveller,' Monkey says. 'And I'm on

.... journey to India with .... monk. He's

.... interesting young man.'

8 Complete the text with *a, an* or *the*.

One day, Tripitaka, Monkey and Pigsy come to **a)** ....a........ river. It's called

b) .... River of **c)** .... Flowing Sand. Suddenly **d)** ....

three travellers hear **e)** .... noise from **f)** .... water. In front of them,

there's **g)** .... angry river monster with **h)** .... long spade in its hand,

and **i)** .... water bottle at its side. Pigsy hits **j)** .... monster on

k) .... head with his muck rake, but it goes under **l)** .... water again.

Tripitaka sits down on **m)** .... rock. 'How are we going to go across

n) .... river now?' he thinks.

GRAMMAR

GRAMMAR CHECK

Everybody, someone, nothing, etc.

We use everybody, everyone, and everything to talk about 'all the people' and 'all the things'.

Stand back everybody! Leave everything to me!

We use nobody, no one, and nothing to talk about 'no person or people' and 'no thing or things'.

Nobody knows the story. My kingdom is nothing without you.

We use somebody, someone, and something to talk about an unknown person or thing.

There's someone here. He found something in the well.

The words everybody and everyone mean the same. This is true of nobody / no one, and of somebody / someone.

9 Choose the correct words to complete the sentences.

a The king told his story: There was no food in his kingdom, and everyone / someone was hungry.

b People had *nothing / everything* for their dinner.

c One day, *nobody / somebody* came to the king.

d He said *nothing / something* important.

e He could make rain clouds. Soon *everything / nothing* in the country was green again.

f People ate food from the farms. *Somebody / Nobody* was hungry now.

g Suddenly, *everyone / someone* felt happy again.

0 Complete the text with *everybody, everything, nobody, nothing, somebody,* or *something*.

Tripitaka talks to Monkey and tells him **a)** .....everything.. .'**b)** ....is now the King of Cockadoodle,' says Tripitaka. 'But that man is an imposter, and **c)** ....knows this. The true king can do **d)** ....about it!'

Then Monkey learns **e)** ....interesting: The Prince wants to visit the country with all his men, and **f)** ....is meeting near the monastery.

'What can I do now?' Monkey thinks.

GRAMMAR CHECK

Past Simple

We use the Past Simple for things that happened at a specific time in the past, and are now finished.

We add –ed to most regular verbs to make the Past Simple. When a verb ends in –e, we add only –d.

When a verb ends in consonant + y, we change y into i, and add –ed.

Guanyin visited an old monastery.   *Lotus Flower changed into a demon.*

Blue Orchid cried a lot when she was a prisoner.

Some verbs have irregular pasts.

The little monkeys fought the red demon.   *The travellers came to a big river.*

We make the Past Simple negative with didn't (did not) + the infinitive without *to*.

Monkey didn't feel afraid.

11 Complete Tripitaka's text with the Past Simple of the verbs in the box.

| arrive   answer   ~~become~~   begin   cry   fall   go   hear   hit   leave |
| look for   not come   run away   say   see   smile   take   travel |

One day, we all **a)** ...become... very angry with Monkey, and he
b) .... from us. The next day, Sandy, Pigsy, and
I **c)** .... along the road to a little village.
  Pigsy **d)** .... and **e)** .... food, but he **f)** ....
back. So we **g)** .... to walk into the village. Suddenly, we
h) .... into a trap, and when we looked up, we **i)** .... two
angry demons over us. 'Help! Help!' I **j)** .... again and again.
  The demons **k)** .... us to a big fire, but just then, Monkey
l) .... on his magic cloud. He **m)** .... the demons with
his staff, and they quickly **n)** .... us.
  'Master, I **o)** .... your cries in my sleep last night!' Monkey
p) .... to me. 'And now I'm here!'
  'Thank you, Monkey,' I **q)** .... him. 'Please don't leave us again!
We need you!' Monkey **r)** .... happily at that.

GRAMMAR CHECK

Sentence adverbials: *at first, later, in the end*, **etc.**

We often use sentence adverbials to tell a story. They link different events, and show their order.

The Emperor put Monkey in the oven at once.

Some days later, the travellers came to a big river.

Monkey didn't move. Then he suddenly jumped up.

12 **Choose the correct words to complete Pigsy's text.**

a) At first / At once, I was the Admiral of Heaven and I did important work. **b)** *At the same time / Now* I became friends with the Moon Goddess. The Emperor **c)** *at first / soon* heard of this, and he said, 'You must leave Heaven **d)** *at once / just then*!' So **e)** *suddenly / at the same time* I was born again on Earth in a monster's body.

A holy woman visited me, and some months **f)** *at first / later* I went to India with a monk and two travellers. We needed to find some holy scrolls.

g) *In the end / At once*, we arrived in India, and we came back with the scrolls.

h) *Now / Just then*, I'm an Altar Boy, and I live happily in Heaven.

13 **Complete Sandy's text with the words in the box.**

At first	In the end	later	Now	soon	Then

a) ..At first.., I was the General of Heaven, but I broke the Emperor's vase. So I was born again on Earth.

b) ....I became a monster in the River of the Flowing Sand. Very **c)** ....a holy woman visited me. I needed to go to India, and to say 'sorry' for the vase. Some time **d)** ...., three travellers arrived, and I went to India with them.

e) ...., we arrived at Buddha's home, and we brought some holy scrolls back to China

f) ...., I'm Master of the Well of Heaven, and I love working with water!

DOMINOES Your Choice

Read *Dominoes* for pleasure, or to develop language skills. It's your choice.

Each *Domino* reader includes:
- a good story to enjoy
- integrated activities to develop reading skills and increase vocabulary
- task-based projects – perfect for CEFR portfolios
- contextualized grammar activities

Each *Domino* pack contains a reader, and an excitingly dramatized audio recording of the story

If you liked this *Domino*, read these:

Sherlock Holmes: The Top Secret Plans
Sir Arthur Conun Doyle

'This telegram is from my brother Mycroft,' said Holmes. 'He wants to speak to me at once about Mr Arthur Cadogan. Do you know this man, Watson?'

'I saw something about him in today's newspaper,' I answered. When a young man dies on a London Underground line, top secret plans for a new British submarine go missing. But who is Cadogan's killer, why did he die, and where are the missing papers? Sherlock Holmes and Doctor Watson must quickly help Mycroft to answer these important questions.

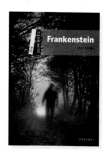

Frankenstein
Mary Shelley

'My name is Victor Frankenstein.'

On a ship in the Arctic, Victor Frankenstein – ill and tired – tells the story of his sad life to the British man of science, Robert Walton. He talks of his family and friends in Geneva, and of his love for beautiful Elizabeth Lavenza. He speaks, too, about the terrible creature that he made from dead body parts when he was a university science student. He hates this monster, which has destroyed his life. But how does the monster feel about its maker?

	CEFR	Cambridge Exams	IELTS	TOEFL iBT	TOEIC
Level 3	B1	PET	4.0	57-86	550
Level 2	A2–B1	KET-PET	3.0-4.0	–	390
Level 1	A1–A2	YLE Flyers/KET	3.0	–	225
Starter & Quick Starter	A1	YLE Movers	1.0–2.0	–	–

You can find details and a full list of books and teachers' resources on our website:
www.oup.com/elt/gradedreaders